Imagine paddling solo, 50 miles for 17 days, in the most shark-infested summer Australia has ever seen; skateboarding 2500 miles for 56 days along the length of Route 66, through the scorching Mojave Desert—at 130°F heat—for 24 hours non-stop; and pushing a 3 tonne pick-up truck 17 miles. Everyone told it was impossible. As an international endurance and being a world record breaking athlete, this is a part of Damien Rider's daily life.

I give thanks to the ocean.

Damien Rider

ONE BREATH MEDITATION

RISE ABOVE PHYSICAL, MENTAL, AND EMOTIONAL STRESS, TO KEEP MOVING FORWARD

AUSTIN MACAULEY PUBLISHERS™

LONDON · CAMBRIDGE · NEW YORK · SHARJAH

Ordering Information:
Quantity sales: special discounts are available on quantity purchases by corporations, associations, and others. For details, contact the publisher at the address below.

Publisher's Cataloguing-in-Publication data
Rider, Damien
One Breath Meditation

ISBN 9781645757627 (Paperback)
ISBN 9781645757610 (Hardback)
ISBN 9781645757634 (ePub e-book)

Library of Congress Control Number: 2020932402

www.austinmacauley.com/us

First Published (2020)
Austin Macauley Publishers LLC
40 Wall Street, 28th Floor
New York, NY 10005
USA

mail-usa@austinmacauley.com
+1 (646) 5125767

Table of Contents

Testimonials

I reached out to Damien to find if this program would help me address the personal challenges that I'd been facing for some time. Practicality and connection with real life is what sets this course apart. You are not bound to a studio or equipment and once you learn the tools, they can be implemented in any situation. Each session logically progressed from the previous session, stretching us further in our breathing and attention, where we slowly built a layering of understanding about our breathing and its connection to our attention. There was nothing mystical or spiritual about the course, it contained simple logical and practiced knowledge and was structured in a way that built up enough to eventually apply it under a real-life, stressful situation. I found the program both intuitive and simple, yet so very powerful. I'm now calmer, less reactive, and starting each day connecting with my breath, allowing a calmer approach to my day. In a complex and busy world, "One Breath Meditation," is a refreshingly simple approach to tap into the basics of our breathing and attention and showing us that we have power and control within us.

Adam Stone

Photographer, Digital Marketing & Small Business Solutions

I found out about the meditation sessions via our local Facebook community page. I had minimal experience with meditation prior to attending Damien's workshop, and was pretty unsure about what to expect. Any trepidation was quickly dispelled upon meeting Damien and the rest of the group. I found it easy to settle into a relaxed but alert state with Damien's guidance and looked forward to the sessions each morning. There was no jargon or difficult techniques, and I found I was able to smoothly integrate Damien's method into my everyday life. In less than a week, my wife shared that she had noticed a change in my reactivity to life's everyday stressors. Moving forward, I've continued to use Damien's techniques, and also found them particularly beneficial during times of physical stress and exertion. I'd highly recommend Damien to any total beginner who's curious about learning to quiet down and focus their mind.

Matt Horton

Orthopedic Clinical Specialist in Arthroplasty Surgery

I attended Damien's "One Breath Meditation" program just as my life was heading into turmoil, my hope being that it would help me through this difficult time. Having done much meditation previously, I found Damien's teaching to be unique and easily applied instantly to any situation as it occurred. Using the ocean as the perfect tool, Damien taught me how to focus, calm my mind, breathe, and relax through stressful, confronting, and uncomfortable emotional, physical, and mental situations. This program has given me much confidence and provided me with immediate strategies to help with stressful situations. I now personally implement these strategies daily and use parts of these strategies with my own work. Damien is a genuine, caring, kind-hearted, empathetic, and inspiring man, whose passion in helping others who are all on a journey of growth, healing and set discovery. I highly recommend the "One Breath Meditation" course to anyone.

Nicola Brewer

I recently joined the "One Breath Meditation" program, after finding myself really run down and stressed out. As air crew in the aviation industry, I work odd shift hours away from home which often change at short notice.

It can make it hard to plan basic things and develop any kind of routine in my life. The "One Breath Meditation" program showed me how to find some peace in the storm. I can't always be sure I'll have the time, space, equipment, or environment to do a 45-minute mediation class in absolute uninterrupted silence. With this, I can use ten minutes in the car or while I walk to find my breath, calm myself, and find the focus that I need to not just survive, but actually enjoy the "right here and now."

Lesley Overland

Foreword

I first met Damien in 2015, shortly after completing his 17-day world record, unassisted 800km paddle from the Gold Coast to Sydney's Bondi Beach. Damien has a dream to make us aware of the endemic child abuse that pervades our society and used his personal journey to draw attention to this issue which shames our society. PACA and Damien's movie, "Heart of the Sea," has continued to draw attention to the issue of the epidemic of child abuse that is endemic to our society. I was privileged to be able to play my small part in "Heart of the Sea" and be a director for the Rider Foundation.

I now know Damien to be a man of inexhaustible passion and integrity; he has the insight and compassion far beyond that of most people.

Damien's survival from a childhood of traumatic, systematic, and ongoing child abuse is nothing short of miraculous. His history is amongst the worst cases that I have come across in almost 40 years of practice as a psychologist, to listen to even brief descriptions of what he endured, leaves a listener severely traumatized. From this pain and trauma, Damien has created and shares a healing journey which demands to be shared with others. Part of this journey has led to this book, which will benefit all who take the time to read it.

A major deficiency in our education has been the lack of teaching essential life skills for our psychological, emotional, and mental health.

Damien's "One Breath Meditation" gives and instructs us all in an essential life skill which should be taught as part of our educational curriculum. "One Breath Meditation" is a part of Damien's "toolkit" of life skills that have enabled him to get through anything – to use his own words.

This meditation exercise, when practiced, allows us to stop the incessant chatter of our overactive and overstimulated mind. His exercise is also a foolproof method of relieving the anxiety and fear that is so frequently felt by us all. Most of us have lived with anxiety for so long that we often hardly notice that we are anxious, until this exercise relieves us of our anxiety. The time we live in is not called the "Age of Anxiety" for nothing.

The importance of learning meditation is best stated by the fact that it allows us to manage and control ourselves, our emotions, our psychological and physical health, and even our spiritual health for those who have faith in that realm. The feeling that regular practice creates is described in many ways. It is called inner peace, calm, and the peace beyond all understanding.

As a scientist, as well as a psychologist, I know that when practiced, "One Breath Meditation" will biologically lower your heartrate and blood pressure, as well as change the wavelength which our brain emits alpha waves, these are the wavelengths emitted when in a state of relaxation.

Damien is also a trailblazer in his use of a relatively new technique which he incorporates into his "One Breath Meditation" called EMDR. Like the initial discoverer of this treatment, Damien noticed his use intuitively of EMDR while on his 800km paddle. Similar to being in the room of 1000 demons, Damien has learnt and gives a skill from his life skills toolkit that will enable us to get through anything, as long as we keep moving, taking one step after another and above all. Remember to breathe!

Love, as always,
Brett F Addison.

About Me

I have been on a journey that no one should have to endure.

For thirty-four years, I was a broken soul, weighed down, and tortured by the demons of my past but today, I'm no longer that man. I found a way to face my past, to do battle with the demons, and to do it head-on.

It was a battle that taught me that we're all capable of overcoming our greatest fears and challenges, that our past, no matter how painful, does not determine our future, and that no matter how many times we have been knocked down, we can keep getting up, to find a way to keep moving forward and to rise above.

My name is Damien Rider. In 2015, I completed an 800-kilometre paddle by hand, from Australia's Gold Coast to Sydney's Bondi Beach.

It was a record-breaking paddle that I completed alone, and unassisted.

For seventeen days, I faced every obstacle the ocean could throw at me. A part of me hoped that if the ocean didn't break me, this extreme challenge would somehow give me the strength to confront my tragic childhood where had I endured years of abuse. Never did I imagine that this personal journey would connect with so many people from around the world and so many others who are trying to find a way to rise above their own challenges.

In the three years since completing the paddle, I have dedicated my life to helping those who are trying to find peace and healing, I continue my humanitarian work to support people who have experienced trauma in their lives, and I will continue to push the boundaries with physical challenges, to share my message globally.

My name is Damien Rider. For 34 years, I was a broken soul, weighed down, and tortured by the demons of my past. But I'm no longer that man.

I found a way to face my past, to do battle with the demons head-on.

I found a way to live life on my terms and to RISE ABOVE.

The Origin of One Breath Meditation

For a moment, try to comprehend paddling solo, 800 kilometers for seventeen days, during the most shark-infested summer Australia has ever experienced. Imagine skateboarding 4000 kilometers for fifty-six days, through the scorching Mojave Desert (enduring temperatures of 55 degrees Celsius), on occasion 24 hours non-stop, along with the entire length of Route 66. Or pushing a 3-tonne pick-up truck for 28 kilometers along the coastline of the Gold Coast Highway, and all after, being told it was impossible?

To get your body to a point where it shuts down before your mind is ready to stop. When you are driven by a cause that is so much bigger than all the personal challenges that you have set for yourself and completed.

As an international endurance and world record-breaking athlete, this is part of my daily life.

"BREATHE, ACCEPT, ADAPT, AND KEEP MOVING FORWARD!"

I use these challenges as a way for me to show people the tools to be able to breathe, accept, adapt, and keep moving forward through adversity.

Founder of the Rider Foundation and PACA – Paddle Against Child Abuse, I have travelled the world, processing and refining my intuitive survival method to now be able to share these tools with you.

In 2016, I proudly created the first Child Abuse Awareness Week for Australia and Thailand and was also chosen as keynote speaker for survivors for the Royal Commission on Institutionalized Responses to Child Sexual Abuse, held in Sydney, Australia. Receiving recognition for my national and international efforts broadcast live to millions across the globe as the final baton bearer for the 2018 Commonwealth Games was my most humbling experience.

Throughout my life, including my athletic challenges, I examined the tools that I intuitively used which were allowing me to remain calm in stressful situations and kept me moving forward. It always came back to having control and understanding of my breath, as a way to regulate the physical, mental, and emotional stress that I was under, without having to stop for long periods of time to compose myself. Meditation has long been around and used by billions of people across the globe as a successful approach to calm the mind. Throughout my twenty-five years in the fitness and wellness industry, I explored many of these methods and techniques that people used to manage stress.

My experience found traditional meditation methods required long periods of time sitting and practicing, then potentially years to achieve a calming state, a state that you can carry throughout your day and through life's unexpected stressful situations.

As an athlete, I recognized that I didn't have the time to sit for 30-90 minutes to compose myself enough to continue on with my challenges. At times, I had to make a split second, sometimes life and death controlled decisions, and it's through this that I became more consciously aware of my "One Breath Meditation."

I have used my years of training myself and others to combine all successful techniques and tested them, not just in my athletic challenges, but also through my daily life challenges. The ability to control my physical, mental, and emotional stress and trauma, made me realize that I had discovered a tool that could help so many people around the world.

During my skate from Chicago to Santa Monica along Route 66, I had a lot of time to think about how I could break down what I do intuitively with the "One Breath Meditation." I then spent the next few years working at some of the most amazing wellness retreats in the world, perfecting my "One Breath Meditation" technique and sharing the tools with others.

The five-level, progressive program of "One Breath Meditation" was created to arm elite athletes, CEOs, government officials, and everyday people with the tools to change any stressed mind or stressful situation into being calm and controlled, simply with one breath.

Once you have a strong connection with this technique, it will allow you the ability to assist in calming the emotions of others around you.

Thank you for giving back to yourself with my "One Breath Meditation," I'm super excited knowing you will explore this tool, and allow your life to be calming, in control, and to live life on your terms.

I'm so proud of you.

Level One

Connect to the Breath

The simple act of breathing can be taken for granted; it is an action we do subconsciously, without thought. Connecting to the breath is important to allow connection to our life source and our emotional energy. When we are babies, we intuitively breathe correctly, all the way down, inflating our belly, and exhaling through our mouth. Through school, peers, teachers, and trauma can cause you to unlearn this skill, reverting to shallow breathing into your chest, therefore losing this connection.

The aim of Level One is to bring you back to your natural breathing performance, train your oxygen capacity to increase without force, and teach you how the breath connection can calm and allow you to control your physical, mental, and emotional levels.

I choose to use the beach and the ocean during the "One Breath Meditation" for the negative ions from the ocean, increased oxygen, the grounding nature of the sand between your toes, and also for the continual moving and changing of the ocean. The ocean is a powerful source and I find the stormier the ocean, the calmer the mind. The ocean can be mesmerizing with its forever changing motion, similar to sitting around a campfire, quietly watching the flames.

"One Breath Meditation," is a progressive program in which you will be taken on a journey to connect with your breath. Using the elements, your focus will shift, then draw back again to a strong connection with your breath and yourself in the moment.

The walking component of Level One will be done at a pace just above your comfort zone.

Thank you for taking time out for yourself to learn the "One Breath Meditation" and enjoy the journey.

Level 1

"Start by looking out to the ocean, watching the movement of the water and the waves."

1 minute/9 breaths.

1. Now take up a comfortable position sitting down, with your back straight and head comfortably looking forward.

2. Allow your arms and hands to sit in their natural position in front of you.

   30 seconds/4 breaths.

   "Now close your eyes."

3. Begin to breathe calmly with nothing forced.

4. When you breathe in, your breath draws in through your nose and all the way down until your belly inflates, then allow it to flow all the way out, unforced through your mouth.

5. Your chest or shoulders shouldn't be rising and only with minimal movement.

6. Breathe in through your nose all the way down inflating your belly, then allow it to flow all the way out, unforced through your mouth.

   1 minute/9 breaths.

7. Again, breathe in through your nose all the way down inflating your belly, allow the air to flow all the way out, unforced and through your mouth.

8. Think about the air as it travels through your nose, all the way down, it turns around and is gently released through the soft mouth as your belly deflates.

30 seconds/4 breaths.

1 breath.

9. This time on the breath in, count how many beats it takes to draw in the air to expand your belly, hold for one beat and slowly, with control count, as the air is released out through a soft mouth.

1 breath.

10. Again, draw your breath in all the way down, extend it by two more beats on the inhale, inflate your belly, hold for two beats, and slowly release through a soft mouth, extending the exhale by two more beats.

1 breath.

11. Again, draw your breath in all the way down, extend it by two more beats on the inhale, inflate your belly, hold for two beats, and slowly release through a soft mouth, extending the exhale by two more beats.

1 breath.

12. Again, draw your breath in all the way down, extend it by two more beats on the inhale, inflate your belly, hold for two beats, and slowly release through a soft mouth, extending the exhale by two more beats.

1 breath.

13. Again, draw your breath in all the way down, extend it by two more beats on the inhale, inflate your belly, hold for two beats, and slowly release through a soft mouth, extending the exhale by two more beats.

1 breath.

14. Again, draw your breath in all the way down, extend it by two more beats on the inhale, inflate your belly, hold for two beats, and slowly release through a soft mouth, extending the exhale by two more beats.

15. Once your air is all the way out, take your breathing to a calm and gentle breath, creating a smooth and seamless transition from inhale to exhale. Nothing forced, remain connected with your breath.
1 minute/9 breaths.

"Keeping your eyes closed, you are now turning your focus to sound."

1. Start to focus on the sound of the ocean.
2. Visualize the movement of the ocean. The swell moves toward the shore, the waves break, the water laps up onto the shore, and the water is drawn back out. Again, another wave breaks. Was the wave bigger this time?
3. Keeping your eyes closed, open your mind, and focus on your listening, allow the ocean to become louder and more visual. Hear the changes it makes from waves breaking on the shore and drawing back out to meet the next one.
30 seconds/4 breaths.
4. Keeping your eyes closed, stretch out your mind, and hearing to focus only on the ocean.
1 minute.

5.   You are going to connect back with one breath, inhale deeply through your nose to inflate your belly.

6.   Hold for two beats.

7.   And release gently through a soft mouth with nothing forced.

8.   Calm your breathing from inhale to exhale, keeping your face relaxed on every exhale.

1 minute/9 breaths.

9.   Again, with one breath, draw in deeply through your nose to inflate your belly.

10.   Hold for two beats.

11.   And release gently through a soft mouth with nothing forced.

12.   Calm your breathing from inhale to exhale, keeping your face relaxed on every exhale. Make a seamless transition from inhale to exhale.

13.   Focus only on your breath and how smooth you can make it.

14.   1 minute/9 breaths.

"Keeping your eyes closed, shift your focus onto touch."

15.   Turn your focus to the wind. Feel the direction it is coming from. Is it hitting you on the face?

16.   Is it hitting you on the legs?

17.   Is it hitting you on the hand?

18.   Is it pulsing, or blowing with a consistent breeze? Is it cool, or is it warm?

19.   30 seconds/4 breaths.

20. Keeping your eyes closed, stretch out your sense of touch, feel the wind. It's the only thing you are going to focus on.

1 minute/9 breaths.

1 breath

21. Now connect back with your breath. Draw in with one breath deeply through your nose to inflate your belly.

22. Hold for two beats.

23. And release gently through a soft mouth with nothing forced.

24. Calm your breathing from inhale to exhale, keeping your face relaxed on every exhale.

30 seconds/4 breaths.

1 breath

25. Again, draw one breath in deeply through your nose to inflate your belly.

26. Hold for two beats.

27. And release gently through a soft mouth with nothing forced.

28. Calm your breathing from inhale to exhale, keeping your face relaxed on every exhale, making a seamless transition from inhale to exhale.

29. Focus only on your breath and how smooth you can make it.

1 minute/9 breaths.

"Now, you are going to connect your breath with your physical self."

2 breaths.

30. Exaggerating your inhale slightly, breathe down and inflate your belly and hold for a beat. As you do, focus on the top of your head, just letting go and exhale, calm and controlled through a soft mouth.

2 breaths.

31. Now draw down and inflate your belly, hold for a beat, and think about letting go of your face, as you release your breath through a soft mouth.

2 breaths.

32. Move your focus down to your shoulders and again, with a slightly exaggerated inhale, draw your breath down, hold for a beat, release your shoulders, and exhale gently through a soft mouth.

2 breaths.

33. Shift focus to your back, and again with a slightly exaggerated inhale, draw your breath down, feeling your lower back expand, hold for a beat, release your back, and exhale gently through a soft mouth letting it go.

2 breaths.

34. Moving to your belly inhale again, drawing your breath down, feeling your belly expand, hold, release, and exhale gently through a soft mouth, letting it go and feel yourself sink into the earth.

2 breaths.

35. Focus now on your glutes, as you draw your breath down, feel your glutes begin to release and allow them to sink into the earth with a gentle and controlled exhale through a soft mouth.

2 breaths.

36.   Move your focus to your legs, drawing your breath down, hold for a beat, then release your legs and allow them to sink into the earth as you exhale.

2 breaths.

37.   Now focus on releasing your feet, as you breathe in, hold, and exhale through a soft mouth, letting your feet sit in their natural positions, sinking into the earth.

2 breaths.

38.   Release your arms and inhale all the way down to your belly, hold, and let them go.

2 breaths.

39.   Finally, your hands, inhale, hold and exhale, allowing them to release to their natural position.

40.   Staying connected to your breath, inhale, and exhale with a smooth, seamless transition. As you exhale, let go and feel yourself sink into the earth, allowing gravity to connect your whole physical being to the grounding of the earth.

30 seconds/4 breaths.

1 breath.

41.   Connect back with your breath. Draw in deeply through your nose to inflate your belly.

42.   Hold for two beats and release gently through a soft mouth with nothing forced. Breaths.

43.   Calm your breathing from inhale to exhale, keeping your face relaxed on every exhale.

1 breath.

44. Again, draw in deeply through your nose to inflate your belly.

45. Hold for two beats, and release gently through a soft mouth with nothing forced.

46. Calm your breathing from inhale to exhale, keeping your face relaxed on every exhale, making a seamless transition from inhale to exhale.

1 minute/9 breaths.

47. Focus only on your breath and how smooth you can make it.

"Staying connected with your breath, open your eyes, and slowly stand up and walk towards to water's edge."

48. You are going to begin walking at a pace of intent along the shoreline, remaining connected to your breath. Remain calm and breathing with long drawn-out breaths, all the way down, inflating your belly and slowly release through a soft mouth.

49. If your mind starts to wander, take a look out to the ocean, and let your eyes take in all that you see, then connect back with your breath, continuing forward.

50. Walk in silence for fifteen minutes, focusing only on your breath.

51. Once you hear my voice again, take a minute to connect with your breath and share something you are proud of.

52. You can share it to yourself, to the ocean, or to someone if they are with you.

"Let's start walking."

15 minutes.

53. Nice walking.

54. Now take a minute to calm yourself with your breath.

1 minute/9 breaths.

55. Feel free to share something you are proud of.

30 seconds.

"Thank you for sharing."

56. Make your way back at a comfortable pace and enjoy the walk.

17 minutes.

"Amazing work."

57. You have completed Level One of "One Breath Meditation," I am so proud of you, and look forward to sharing level two with you.

Homework:

58. Remember to breathe, be conscious of your breath, inflating your belly with long, drawn-out breaths.

"Have an amazing day."

Level Two

Connect to the Sense of Sight

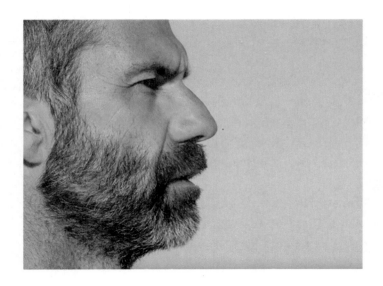

We have begun the connection to your breath, adding in the natural elements and senses of touch and sound, as well as the connection of your breath to calm your whole physical being.

In Level Two, you will continue to explore the elements and senses by adding in the sense of sight

I will begin to busy your mind in a calm and controlled state, allowing you to keep emotionally calm, whilst your mind absorbs all the information the ocean movement offers. I will then detach you from your busy mind and back to the connection of your breath. This process will begin to simulate your busy daily life and by connecting to your breath, you can detach from your busy mind and ground yourself while the world moves frantically in front of your eyes.

You will walk at a faster pace, reaching a further distance than in day one but in the same amount of time.

Level 2

59. Before you begin today, I would like you to take a minute to look out to the ocean. Take in all that you see, look at the waves, see how they are breaking, watch the motion of the water movement. While you do this, slow your inhale and exhale to long, drawn-out, unforced breaths.

1 minute/7 breaths.

60. Now sitting down, taking up a comfortable position with your back straight and head comfortably looking forward. Allow your arms and hands to sit comfortably in front of you.

30 seconds/3 breaths.

"Now allow your eyes to close."

61.   Begin connecting to your breath, deeply and calmly
        with nothing forced.

1 minute/7 breaths.

62.   Breathe in through your nose all the way down so
        that your belly inflates, then allow it to flow all the
        way out, unforced through your mouth.

63.   Your chest and shoulders shouldn't be rising and
        only with minimal movement.

64.   Again, breathe in through your nose all the way
        down inflating your belly, then allow it to flow all
        the way out, unforced through your mouth.

65.   Think about the air as it travels through your nose,
        all the way down, turns around, and is gently
        released through the soft mouth as your belly
        deflates.

30 seconds/3 breaths.

1 breath.

66.   This time on the breath in, count how many beats it
        takes to draw in the air to expand your belly, then
        hold for a beat, and slowly with control, count as
        the air is released through a soft mouth.

1 breath.

67.   This time when you breathe, increase the inhale by
        two more beats on the way down to expand and
        inflate your belly. Hold for two beats and slowly

control the release through a soft mouth, extending it by two more beats.

1 breath.

68.   Again, draw your breath all the way down, extend your inhale in by two more beats inflating your belly, hold for two beats, and slowly release through a soft mouth by two more beats.

1 breath.

69.   Again, draw your breath all the way down, extend your inhale in by two more beats inflating your belly, hold for two beats, and slowly release through a soft mouth by two more beats.

1 breath.

70.   Again, draw your breath all the way down, extend your inhale in by two more beats inflating your belly, hold for two beats, and slowly release through a soft mouth by two more beats.

71.   Once all your air is out, take your breathing to a calm and gentle breath, with a smooth and seamless transition from inhale to exhale. Nothing forced and staying connected with your breath.

1 minute/7 breaths.

"You are now going to connect your breath with your physical self."

2 breaths.

72.   Exaggerating your inhale slightly, breathe down, inflate your belly for two breaths and hold for a beat. As you do, you are going to focus on the top

of your head, just letting go and exhale calm and controlled through a soft mouth.

2 breaths.

73.   This time, draw down and inflate your belly, hold for a beat, and think about letting go of your face as you release your breath through a soft mouth.

2 breaths.

74.   Move your focus down to your shoulders, inhale all the way down, inflating your belly, holding for two beats, release your shoulders, and exhale gently through a soft mouth.

2 breaths.

75.   Moving down to your arms, two times inhale all the way down, inflating your belly, holding for two beats, release your arms, and exhale gently through a soft mouth.

2 breaths.

76.   Moving down to your hands, two times inhale all the way down, inflating your belly, holding for two beats, then release your hands and exhale gently through a soft mouth.

2 breaths.

77.   Now direct your attention to your upper back, two times inhale all the way down, inflating your belly, holding for two beats, release your upper back, and exhale gently through a soft mouth.

2 breaths.

78.   Focusing on your chest, again two times inhale all the way down, inflating our belly, holding for two beats, release your chest, and exhale gently through a soft mouth.

2 breaths.

79. Moving down to your lower back, two times inhale all the way down, inflating your belly, holding for two beats, release your lower back, and exhale gently through a soft mouth.

2 breaths.

80. Now to your belly, two times inhale all the way down, inflating your belly, holding for two beats, release your belly, and exhale gently through a soft mouth.

2 breaths.

81. Moving down to your glutes, two times inhale all the way down, inflating your belly, holding for two beats, release your glutes, and exhale gently through a soft mouth.

2 breaths.

82. Bring your focus to your legs, two times inhale all the way down, inflating your belly, holding for two beats, release your legs, and exhale gently through a soft mouth.

2 breaths.

83. Now move to your feet, two times inhale all the way down, inflating your belly, holding for two beats, release your feet allowing them to sit in their natural position, and exhale gently through a soft mouth.

4 breaths.

84. Staying connected to your breath, inhale and exhale with a smooth, seamless transition and as you exhale, allow yourself to let go and feel yourself sink into the earth. Allow gravity to connect your whole physical being to the grounding of the earth.

1 breath.

85.   Now it's time to connect back with your breath. Inhale deeply with one breath through your nose to inflate your belly.

86.   Hold for two beats.

87.   And release gently through a soft mouth with nothing forced.

30 seconds.

88.   Calm your breathing from inhale to exhale, keeping your face relaxed on every exhale.

1 breath.

89.   Again, you are going to connect with one, deep breath through your nose to inflate your belly.

90.   Hold for two beats.

91.   And release gently through a soft mouth with nothing forced.

92.   Calm your breathing from inhale to exhale, keeping your face relaxed on every exhale. Making a seamless transition from inhale to exhale.

30 seconds/3 breaths.

93.   Focus only on your breath and how smooth you can make it.

1 minute/7 breaths.

"Keeping your eyes closed, it's now time to focus on sound."

94.   Turn your attention to the sound of the ocean, visualizing the movement of the ocean. The swell moves towards the shore, the waves break, the

water laps up onto the shore, and the water is drawn back out. Again, another wave breaks.

95.   Is it bigger this time?

1 minute/7 breaths.

96.   Keeping your eyes closed, open your mind and hearing, and allow the ocean to become louder and more visual. Hear the changes of the waves breaking on the shore and drawing back out to meet the next one.

30 seconds/4 breaths.

97.   Keeping your eyes closed, stretch out your mind and hearing to focus only on the ocean.

1 minute/7 breaths.

1 breath.

98.   Now you are going to connect back with one breath. Inhale deeply through your nose to inflate your belly.

99.   Hold for two beats.

100.   And release gently through a soft mouth with nothing forced.

101.   Calm your breathing with long, drawn-out breaths from inhale to exhale, relaxing your face on every exhale.

1 minute/7 breaths.

1 breath.

102.   Again, draw in with one breath firmly through your nose to inflate your belly.

103.   Hold for two beats.

104.   And release gently through a soft mouth with nothing forced.

105.   Calm your breathing from inhale to exhale, keeping your face relaxed on every exhale, making a seamless transition from inhale to exhale.

106.   Focus only on your breath and how smooth you can make it.

1 minute/7 breaths.

"Keeping your eyes closed, you are going to focus on touch now."

107.   I'd like you to focus on the sun. Feel the direction it is coming from. Is it hitting you on the face?

Is it hitting you on the legs?

Is it hitting you on the hands?

Think of where it is hitting you the most and focus on that spot. Can you feel the heat of the sun increase?

1 minute/7 breaths.

108.   Keeping your eyes closed, draw attention to your sense of touch and feel the sun so it's the only thing you are focused on.

1 minute.

1 breath.

109.   Now connect back with your breath. Inhale with one breath deeply through your nose to inflate your belly.

110.   Hold for two beats.

111.   And release gently through a soft mouth with nothing forced.

112.   Calm your breathing from inhale to exhale, keeping your face relaxed on every exhale.

1 minute/7 breaths.

1 breath.

113. Now connect back with your breath. Inhale in with one breath deeply through your nose to inflate your belly.

114. Hold for two beats.

115. And release gently through a soft mouth with nothing forced.

116. Calm your breathing from inhale to exhale, keeping your face relaxed on every exhale, making a seamless transition from inhale to exhale.

117. Focus only on your breath and how smooth you can make it.

2 minute/14 breaths.

"You are now going to work on sight."

118. When you are ready, open your eyes, slowly stand up, and walk towards the water's edge.

119. Allow your eyes to move from left to right naturally, taking in all of the detail that you are seeing.

120. See the white caps, the waves breaking, the birds flying by, the swell, how the wind is moving the top of the water, the horizon, how the sun is hitting the water.

121. Let your eyes quickly dart from left to right to take it all in.

1 minute/7 breaths.

1 breath.

122. You are now going to connect back with one breath. Inhale deeply through your nose to inflate your belly.

123. Hold for two beats.

124. And release gently through a soft mouth with nothing forced.

125. Calm your breathing with long, drawn-out breaths from inhale to exhale, keep relaxing your face on every exhale.

1 minute/7 breaths.

126. This time, as you look out to the ocean, I would like you to consciously tell yourself what you are seeing. Tell yourself in exact detail what you are seeing. Note how the waves break on the shore and the whitewash rolls and tumbles towards the shore before drawing back out to meet the next wave.

127. How is the direction of the wind affecting the water? How is the sun making the water and waves sparkle?

128. Busy your mind with the activity in front of you.

1 minute/7 breaths.

1 breath.

129. You are going to connect back with one breath. Inhale in deeply through your nose to inflate your belly.

130. Hold for two beats.

131. And release gently through a soft mouth with nothing forced.

132. Calm your breathing with long, drawn-out breaths from inhale to exhale, keep relaxing your face on every exhale.

1 minute/7 breaths.

133. Now it's time to begin your walk. While you are walking, I'd like you to stay connected to your breath, remaining nice and calm, breathing with long, drawn-out breaths all the way down, inflating your belly, and slowly release through a soft mouth.

134. Walking at a faster pace than day one.

135. If your mind starts to wander, take a look out to the ocean, and let your eyes take in all that you see, then connect back with your breath, continuing forward. Walk for fifteen minutes in silence, focusing only on your breath.

136. Once you have walked for fifteen minutes, take a minute, and connect with your breath and share something you are grateful for.

137. You can share it to yourself, to the ocean, or to someone if they are with you.

"Let's start walking."

15 minutes.

"Nice walking."

138. Take a minute to calm yourself with your breath.

1 minute/5 breaths.

139. Feel free to share something you are grateful for.

30 seconds.

"Thank you for sharing."

Make your way back at a comfortable pace and enjoy your walk.

17 minutes.

"Amazing work."

You have completed Level Two of "One Breath Meditation"; I am proud of you and look forward to sharing Level Three with you.

Homework:
Consciously remind yourself to remember to connect with one breath, for five separate times in the day.
Inhale firmly through your nose to inflate your belly. Hold for two beats.
And release gently through a soft mouth with nothing forced.
Also, keep up your conscious breathing, inflating your belly with calm, long, drawn-out breaths.

"Have an amazing day."

Level Three

Connect to Vibrations to Control Your Breath

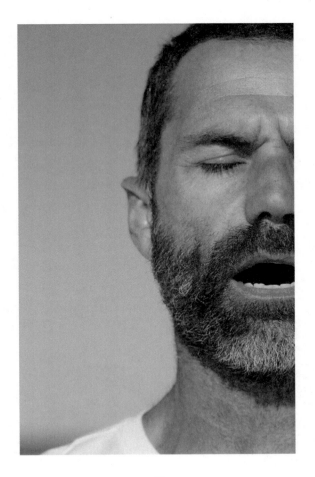

This level will see you adding a hum and the Mantra Om, the vibrations help to control the pace of your exhale. It also allows you to feel where your air is beginning to exhale from. Be confident with your vibrations during the hum and Mantra Om, this will build the confidence with your breath and a stronger controlling connection.

On the walk, experiment with the new controlled exhale, with and without the hum. Walking at a faster pace, while keeping your breath deep and calm from inhale to exhale.

Level 3

140.   Before you begin today, allow a minute to look out to the ocean.

141.   Take in all that you see, look at the waves, see how they are breaking, watch the motion of the water's movement. While you do this, slow your inhale and exhale, to long, drawn-out breaths.

142.   Lengthen your breaths so that you perform less breaths per minute.

1 minute/5 breaths.

143.   Now sitting down, take up a comfortable position with your back straight and head comfortably looking forward. Allow your arms and hands to sit comfortably in front of you.

30 seconds/3 breaths.

"Take a moment now to close your eyes."

144.   Begin connecting to your breath nice and calmly with nothing forced.

1 minute/5 breaths.

145. Inhale through your nose all the way down, inflating your belly, then allow it to flow all the way out, unforced out your mouth.

146. Your chest or shoulders shouldn't be rising and only with minimal movement.

147. Inhale through your nose all the way down, inflating your belly, then allow it to flow all the way out, unforced out your mouth.

148. Again, breathe in through your nose all the way down, inflating your belly, then allow it to flow all the way out, unforced through your mouth.

149. Think about the air as it travels through your nose, all the way down, turns around and is gently released through the soft mouth as your belly deflates.

30 seconds/3 breaths.

1 breath.

150. This time on your inhale, count how many beats it takes to draw the air in to expand your belly, then hold for two beats and slowly with control, count as the air is released through a soft mouth.

1 breath.

151. Again, draw your breath all the way down, extend it by two more beats on the inhale, inflating your belly, hold for two beats, and slowly release through a soft mouth, lengthening the exhale by two more beats.

1 breath.

152.   This time, draw your breath all the way down, extend it by two more beats, hold for two beats, relax your face as you release slowly through a soft mouth, extending by two more beats.

1 breath.

153.   Again, draw your breath all the way down, extend in by two more beats, hold for two beats, relax your face as you release slowly through a soft mouth, extending by two more beats.

1 breath.

154.   Again, draw your breath all the way down, extend in by two more beats, hold for two beats, relax your face as you release slowly through a soft mouth, extending by two more beats.

155.   Once your air is all the way out, take your breathing to a calm and gentle breath, with a smooth and seamless transition, from inhale to exhale.

156.   Nothing forced and stay connected with your breath.

1 minute/5 breaths.

"Now you are going to connect your breath with your physical self."

2 breaths.

157.   Exaggerating your inhale slightly, breathe down, inflate your belly for two breaths and hold for a beat. As you do, you are going to focus on the top of your head, just letting go and exhale, calm and controlled through a soft mouth.

2 breaths.

158. This time, draw down and inflate your belly, hold for a beat, and think about letting go of your face as you release your breath through a soft mouth.

2 breaths.

159. Move down to your shoulders, two times inhale all the way down, inflating your belly, holding for two beats, release your shoulders, and exhale gently through a soft mouth.

2 breaths.

160. Moving down to your arms, two times inhale all the way down, inflating your belly, holding for two beats, release your arms, and exhale gently through a soft mouth.

2 breaths.

161. Now moving down to your hands, two times inhale all the way down, inflating your belly, holding for two beats, release your hands and exhale gently through a soft mouth.

2 breaths.

162. Move now to your upper back, two times inhale all the way down, inflating your belly, holding for two beats, release your upper back, and exhale gently through a soft mouth.

2 breaths.

163. Now moving to your chest, two times inhale all the way down, inflating your belly, holding for two beats, release your chest, and exhale gently through a soft mouth.

2 breaths.

164. Move down to your lower back, two times inhale all the way down, inflating your belly, holding for two beats, release your lower back, and exhale gently through a soft mouth.

2 breaths.

165. Now to your belly, two times inhale all the way down, inflating your belly, holding for two beats, release your belly, and exhale gently through a soft mouth.

2 breaths.

166. Move down to your glutes, two times inhale all the way down, inflating your belly, holding for two beats, release your glutes, and exhale gently through a soft mouth.

2 breaths.

167. Move to your legs, two times inhale all the way down, inflating your belly, holding for two beats, release your legs, and exhale gently through a soft mouth.

2 breaths.

168. Move down to your feet, two times inhale all the way down, inflating your belly, holding for two beats, release your feet, allowing them to sit in their natural position, and exhale gently through a soft mouth.

4 breaths.

169. Staying connected to your breath, inhale and exhale with a smooth, seamless transition and as you exhale, let go and feel yourself sink into the earth. Allow gravity to connect your whole physical being to the grounding of the earth.

"Keeping your eyes closed you are now going to focus on sound."

170. Shift your focus to the sound of the ocean. Visualize the movement of the ocean. The swell moves towards the shore, the waves break, the water laps up onto the shore, and the water is drawn back out. Again, another wave breaks. Is it bigger this time?

1 minute/5 breaths.

171. Keeping your eyes closed, open your mind and hearing, and allow the ocean to become louder and more visual. Hear the changes it makes from waves breaking on the shore and drawing back out to meet the next one.

30 seconds/3 breaths.

172. Keeping your eyes closed, stretch out your mind and hearing to focus only on the ocean.

1 minute/5 breaths.

173. 1 breath.

174. Now you're going to connect back with one breath. Draw in deeply through your nose to inflate your belly.

175. Hold for two beats.

176. And release gently through a soft mouth with nothing forced.

1 breath.

177. Again, inhale with one breath deeply through your nose to inflate your belly.

178. Hold for two beats.

179. And release gently through a soft mouth with nothing forced.
180. Calm your breathing from inhale to exhale, keeping your face relaxed on every exhale. Making a seamless transition from inhale to exhale.
181. Focus only on your breath and how smooth you can make it.
182. As you exhale, allow your whole body to relax and sink into the sand. Let gravity take hold.

1 minute/5 breaths.

183. I'd like you to focus on the sun.
184. Feel the direction it is coming from. Is it hitting you on the face?
185. Is it hitting you on the legs?
186. Is it hitting you on the hands?
187. Think of where it is hitting you the most and focus on that spot, can you feel the heat of the sun increase?

1 minute/5 breaths.

188. Keeping your eyes closed, draw towards the sense of touch. Concentrate on feeling the heat of the sun so it's the only thing you are focused on.

1 minute/5 breaths.

1 breath.

189. Now connect back with one breath. Inhale deeply through your nose to inflate your belly.
190. Hold for two beats.
191. And release gently through a soft mouth with nothing forced.

1 breath.

192. Again, draw in one breath deeply through your nose to inflate your belly.

193. Hold for two beats.

194. And release gently through a soft mouth with nothing forced.

195. Calm your breathing from inhale to exhale, keeping your face relaxed on every exhale, making a seamless transition from inhale to exhale.

196. Focus only on your breath and how smooth you can make it.

2 minute/10 breaths.

"You are now going to work on sight."

197. When you are ready, open your eyes, slowly stand up, and walk towards the water's edge.

198. Allow your eyes to move from left to right naturally, taking in all the information that you are seeing.

199. See the white caps, the waves breaking, the birds flying by, the swell, how the wind moves the top of the water, the horizon, how the sun is hitting the water.

200. Let your eyes quickly dart from left to right to take it all in.

1 minute/5 breaths.

1 breath

201. Now connect back with one breath, if you need a stronger connection, just close your eyes as you inhale deeply through your nose to inflate your belly.

202.   Hold for two beats.

203.   And release gently through a soft mouth with nothing forced.

204.   Calm your breathing with long, drawn-out breaths from inhale to exhale. Start at the top of your head and on every exhale, think of water running down your head, down your body, and all the way into the sand. Relaxing every part of your physical being as you feel the water make its way down.

205.   1 minute/5 breaths.

206.   This time, look out to the ocean, consciously tell yourself in detail what you are seeing. How do the waves break on the shore? How does the whitewash roll and tumble before drawing back out to meet the next wave? How does the direction of the wind affect the water? How is the sun making the water and waves sparkle?

207.   Busy your mind with the activity in front of you.

2 minute/10 breaths.

1 breath.

208.   You are going to connect back with one breath. Inhale deeply through your nose to inflate your belly.

209.   Hold for two beats.

210.   And release gently through a soft mouth with nothing forced.

211.   Calm your breathing with long, drawn-out breaths from inhale to exhale, keep relaxing your face on every exhale.

212.

1 minute/5 breaths.

"You are going to work on vibrations."

2 minute/10 breaths.

213.   This time, draw in all the way down and on the exhale, with your lips together, hum the air all the way out in one consistent motion, until all the air has been hummed out.

214.   You are going to do this eight times.

215.   As you do, feel the vibrations through your body. Starting with your head and moving the vibrations so they become stronger in your belly, in your legs, and in your back.

1 breath.

216.   Connecting back with one breath. Inhale deeply through your nose to inflate your belly.

217.   Hold for two beats.

218.   And release gently through a soft mouth with nothing forced.

219.   Calm your breathing with long, drawn-out breaths from inhale to exhale, relaxing your whole physical being from your head, down your body, and sinking into the earth on every exhale.

1 minute/5 breaths.
2 minutes/10 breaths.

220.   This time, inhale all the way down, and on the exhale, starting with your lips together, hum the air to begin the breathe out and slowly open your mouth to create the mantra Om sound.

221.   Each exhale of Om, I would like you to increase the volume of sound projected so you can feel the vibrations over your whole physical being.

222.   You are going to do this eight times.

1 breath.

223.   Now connect back with one breath. Inhale deeply through your nose to inflate your belly.

224.   Hold for two beats.

225.   And release gently through a soft mouth with nothing forced.

226.   Calm your breathing with long, drawn-out breaths from inhale to exhale, relaxing your whole physical being from your head, down your body, and sinking into the earth on every exhale.

1 minute/5 breaths.

227.   It's now time to begin your walk.

228.   While you are walking, stay connected to your breath, remaining nice and calm, breathing with long, drawn-out breaths, all the way down, inflating your belly, and slowly release through a soft mouth. Think of how slow, calm, and controlled the exhale was while humming and performing the mantra OM.

229.   This time, walk at a faster pace so you reach a further distance than days one and two in the same amount of time.

230.   If your mind starts to wander, take a lookout to the ocean, and let your eyes take in all that you see, then connect back with your breath, continuing forward. Continue your walk for 15 minutes in silence, focusing only on your calm breath. Once you reach

15 minutes, take a minute, and connect with your breath, and share something you are going to achieve.

231.   You can share it to yourself, to the ocean, or to someone that you are with.

"Start walking again."

15 minutes.

"Nice walking."

232.   Take a minute to calm yourself with your breath.

1 minute/5 breaths.

233.   Feel free to share something you are going to achieve.

30 seconds.

"Thank you for sharing."

234.   Make your way back at a comfortable pace and enjoy your walk.

17 minutes.

"Amazing work."

You have completed Level Three of "One Breath Meditation"; I am proud of you and look forward to sharing Level Four with you.

Homework:

Is to perform the mantra Om at least five separate times throughout the day and think about how you can control your exhale for a longer breath out. Keep up your conscious breathing, inflating your belly with calm long, drawn-out breaths.

"Have an amazing day."

Level Four

Disconnect from Monkey Mind

We have all experienced the Monkey Mind, where our active thoughts take over our emotions and actions. All Monkey wants is a job task. In Level Four, I will take you through a process combining sights, sounds, and self-talk to activate and over-stimulate your mind. You will then connect with your breath and disconnect from the active mind and sights which help trigger the process subconsciously in daily life, growing the connection to the "One Breath Meditation."

Your walk will be performed at a fast pace with intent. You will increase the distance of the previous levels whilst maintaining a strong connection with your breath, your mind, and physical self-calm, allowing your body do the work.

235.   Today, you are going to begin by standing at the water's edge. Consciously slow your long, drawn-out breaths again for your inhale and exhale.

236.   Begin connecting to your breath calmly with nothing forced.

1 minute/4 breaths.

237.   When you inhale, breathe in through your nose all the way down, inflating your belly, and then allow it to flow all the way out, unforced through your mouth.

238.   Your chest or shoulders shouldn't be rising and only with minimal movement.

239.   Breathe in through your nose all the way down, inflating your belly, then allow it to flow all the way out, unforced through your mouth.

240.   Again, breathe in through your nose all the way down, inflating your belly, then allow it to flow all the way out, unforced through your mouth.

241.   Think about the air as it travels through your nose, all the way down, turns around and is gently released through the soft mouth as your belly deflates.

30 seconds/2 breaths.

1 breath.

242.   You are going to connect strongly with one breath. Inhale deeply through your nose to inflate your belly.

243.   Hold for two beats.

244.   And release gently through a soft mouth with nothing forced.

1 breath.

245.   Again, you are going to connect with one breath. Inhale deeply through your nose to inflate your belly.

246.   Hold for two beats.

247.   And release gently through a soft mouth with nothing forced, calming your face.

4 breaths.

248.   Closing your eyes, staying connected to your breath, inhale and exhale with a smooth, seamless transition. As you exhale, let go and feel yourself sink into the earth. Allow gravity to connect your whole physical being to the grounding of the earth.

"You are now going to work on sight."

249.   Open your eyes, stay connected to your breath.

250.   Allow your eyes to move from left to right naturally, take in all the information you are seeing.

251.   See the white caps, the waves breaking, the birds flying by, the swell, how the wind is moving the top of the water, the horizon, how the sun is hitting the water.

252.   Let your eyes quickly dart from left to right to take it all in.

2 minute/8 breaths.

1 breath.

253.   Now you are going to connect back with one breath, inhale deeply through your nose to inflate your belly.

254.   Hold for two beats.

255.   And release gently through a soft mouth with nothing forced.

1 breath.

256.   You are going to form a strong connection to your one breath, if you need a stronger connection, just close your eyes as you inhale deeply through your nose to inflate your belly.

257.   Hold for two beats.

258.   And release gently through a soft mouth with nothing forced.

259.   This time, look out to the ocean, consciously tell yourself in detail what you are seeing. How do the waves break on the shore? How does the whitewash roll and tumble before drawing back out to meet the next wave? How does the direction of the wind

affect the water? How is the sun making the water and waves sparkle?

260. Busy your mind with the activity in front of you.

2 minute/8 breaths.

1 breath.

261. Connect back with one breath. Inhale deeply through your nose to inflate your belly.

262. Hold for two beats.

263. And release gently through a soft mouth with nothing forced.

264. Calm your breathing with long, drawn-out breaths from inhale to exhale, keep relaxing your face on every exhale.

1 minute/4 breaths.

265. Now as you look out to the ocean, I would like you to verbalize in detail exactly what you are seeing. Really open your thoughts with a loud, strong voice. The waves are breaking on the shore and the whitewash is rolling in. Tell yourself how amazing it would be to dive in and what that would feel like. How each wave rolls in and has travelled so far and unstoppable, how no two waves are the same, or how the sun makes the water and waves sparkle. Stay vocal and confident in what you are seeing and feeling.

266. Busy your mind with the activity in front of you.

2 minute/8 breaths.

1 breath.

267.   You are going to connect back with one breath, inhale deeply through your nose to inflate your belly.

268.   Hold for two beats.

269.   And release gently through a soft mouth with nothing forced.

270.   1 breath.

271.   If you need a stronger connection, just close your eyes as you inhale deeply through your nose to inflate your belly.

272.   Hold for two beats.

273.   And release gently through a soft mouth with nothing forced.

274.   Calm your breath, with long, drawn-out breaths from inhale to exhale. Start at the top of your head and on every exhale, think of water running down your head, down your body, and all the way into the sand, relaxing every part of your physical being, as you feel the water making its way down.

275.   Calming your head, calm your shoulders, calm your back, calm your belly, calm your legs, and let gravity ground your whole physical being into the earth.

2 minutes/8 breaths.

"You are now going to work on vibrations."

2 minutes/8 breaths.

276.   This time, draw in all the way down and on the exhale, with your lips together, hum the air all the

way out at one consistent motion, until all the air has been hummed out.

277. You are going to do this eight times.

278. As you do, I'd like you to feel the vibrations through your body. Starting with your head and moving the vibrations so they become stronger in your belly, in your legs, and in your back.

279. Calm your breathing with long, drawn-out breaths from inhale to exhale, keep your whole physical being from your head, down your body and sinking into the earth on every exhale.

1 minute/4 breaths.

2 minutes/8 breaths.

280. This time, inhale all the way down and on the exhale, starting with your lips together, hum the air to begin the breath out and slowly open your mouth to create the mantra Om sound.

281. Each exhale of Om, increase the volume of sound projected so you can feel the vibrations over your whole physical being.

282. You are going to do this eight times.

283. Calm your breathing with long, drawn-out breaths from inhale to exhale, relaxing your whole physical being from your head, down your body, and sinking into the earth on every exhale.

1 minute/4 breaths.

284. Continue the seamless transition of long, drawn-out breaths, from inhale to exhale, calming your whole physical being from your head, down your body, and sinking into the earth on every exhale.

1 minute/4 breaths.

285. Look out to the ocean, connect with all the activity that is happening in front of you. Allow your eyes to move from left to right naturally, take in all the information you are seeing. There is a lot for our minds to get lost in and take over our thoughts. We cannot stop the waves from rolling in, we are looking at an uncontrollable, continual force. The elements, forever changing and moving.

286. Let your eyes quickly dart from left to right to take it all in.

2 minutes/8 breaths.

1 breath.

287. You are going to connect back with one breath, inhale deeply through your nose to inflate your belly.

288. Hold for two beats.

289. And release gently through a soft mouth with nothing forced.

1 breath.

290. If you need a stronger connection, just close your eyes as you inhale deeply through your nose to inflate your belly.

291. Hold for two beats.

292. And release gently through a soft mouth with nothing forced.

4 breaths.

293. This time, keep that same strength of connection to your breath, inhale, hold for two beats, and release through a soft mouth, calming your whole being.

1 breath.

294.   Inhale again with less force, hold for two beats, and release through a soft mouth, calming your whole being.

1 breath.

295.   Inhale with a long, slow breath without force, hold for two beats and release, calming your whole being, feeling the connection as you are grounded with the earth.

296.   Closing your eyes, keeping the strong connection, calm your breathing to a seamless transition from inhale to exhale, calming your whole being on every exhale.

1 minute/4 breaths.

"Slowly open your eyes."

297.   You will now begin your walk.

298.   Walk at a faster pace so you reach a further distance than the previous days, in the same amount of time.

299.   While you are walking, stay connected to your breath, keep controlled and calm breathing with long, drawn-out breaths, all the way down inflating your belly, and then slowly release through a soft mouth.

300.   If your mind starts to wander, draw in to your one breath deeply to connect. Hold for two, calm your mind and physical being, then continue with long, calm breaths from inhale to exhale.

301.   Walk for 15 minutes in silence, focusing only on your calm breath.

302. Once you reach 15 minutes, take a minute, and connect with your breath and share your greatest achievement.

303. You can share it to yourself, to the ocean or to someone if they are with you. Let's start walking.
15 minutes.

"Nice walking."

304. Take a minute to calm ourselves with our breath.
1 minute /4 breaths.

305. Feel free to share your greatest achievement.
30 seconds.

"Thank you for sharing."

306. Make your way back at a comfortable pace, enjoying your walk.
17 minutes.
"Amazing work."

You have completed Level Four of "One Breath Meditation." You are amazing and I look forward to sharing Level Five with you.

Homework:
Start consciously performing the "One Breath Meditation in all situations." Not just in stressful times, but throughout the day in random situations.

In the car, in the shopping line, walking along, or while in a conversation with someone. Keep up your conscious breathing, inflating your belly with calm long, drawn-out breaths.

"Have an amazing day."

Level Five

Controlled Physical and Mental Stress

Physical pain can create negative self-talk and this is usually the reason why we convince ourselves to quit physical activity, such as running.

Level Five will allow you to use the technique learnt in the previous four levels, whilst subjecting yourself to short bursts of controlled physical and mental stress. This will again disconnect you from the physical action and connect with your calm breath, teaching your subconscious to calm your mental and emotional stress under pressure.

Today, you are going to put your body under mild, increased, controlled, physical stress. Begin by standing at the bottom of a steep and long hill, or a long set of stairs. Once you start to make your way up, push yourself to an uncomfortable pace, without over-exerting yourself.

Stay connected with your calm breath and allow the physical body to do the work. Separate the pace of the physical movement from your inhale and exhale.

Once you reach the half-way point, pain may start to set into your legs, creating negative thoughts. While still moving at the same pace, connect with your One Breath, calm your face and physical self, stay connected to your breath and keep moving forward.

Calming yourself before the active exercise while remaining connected to your calm breath will teach you to not over-think what's ahead.

Be proud and confident of your achievements and use the tools learnt during the "One Breath Meditation" while performing your calm breathing before you move off with connection.

Level 5

307. Begin connecting to your breath nice and calmly with nothing forced.

308. Breathe in through your nose all the way down inflating your belly, then allow it to flow all the way out, unforced through your mouth.

309. Think about the air as it travels through your nose, all the way down, turns around and is gently released through the soft mouth as your belly deflates.

2 minutes/8 breaths.

90 seconds/4 breaths.

310. Now close your eyes and count ten beats as you inhale, hold for two beats, then count ten beats on your exhale, keeping the breath slow, calm, and controlled.

1 minute/4 breaths.

311. Take your breath back to the seamless transition from inhale to exhale with nothing forced, calming your mind and your whole physical being on every exhale.

1 minute/4 breaths.

312. Opening your eyes, continue to stay connected to the seamless transition from inhale to exhale, keeping your mind and physical being calm.

313. Stay connected to your calm breath and when you are ready and calm, begin to make your way up the incline, thinking only of your breath.

1 breath.

314. We are going to connect back with one breath, inhale deeply through your nose to inflate your belly.

315. Hold for two beats.

316. And release gently through a soft mouth with nothing forced.

317. Close your eyes for a stronger connection, calming your mind and body with every exhale. Calm your breathing with long, drawn-out breaths from inhale to exhale, keep your whole physical being from your head, down your body, and sinking into the earth on every exhale.

2 minutes/8 breaths.

2 minutes/8 breaths.

318. Open your eyes, staying connected with your breath, you are now going to continue the seamless transition from inhale to exhale. Focus on how calm and smooth you can make it, ensuring all focus is on the calm breath.

319. With your breath and mind calm, I'd like you to share something you are proud of.

30 seconds.

320. Thank you for sharing.

321. I am so proud of you and all you have achieved. You are an amazing person and have the courage to take on any challenge thrown at you. You will

always grow from strength to strength, learning and adapting to keep moving forward.

322.   Please take this time to see the world and start living life on your terms.

"Thank you for allowing me to be a part of your journey."